Seminar 1
Getting started

1. Introductions

A. A quick get-to-know-you quiz

Introduce yourselves by getting each person in the group to answer the following three questions in no more than 60 seconds:

- What's your full name (including middle name/s)?
- Where do you live now and with whom?
- Can you name a book, movie or TV show you have enjoyed in the last three months?

B. Thinking about your life

Now take it in turns to answer one of the following two questions (no more than three minutes for each person). Group members are allowed to ask follow-up questions.

- What have been the turning points in your life so far—the key moments when the road has taken a turn?
- Can you name one or two people (excluding your parents and God) who have had the most influence (for good or ill) in making you into the person you are today? How have they influenced you?

C. Pray

Two or three of the group who feel comfortable to do so can lead in prayer:

- giving thanks for this opportunity to pause and reconsider where our lives are headed
- praying for the members of the group by name, asking God to give insight and clarity and conviction over the duration of the course.

2. Input: Why are we here?

Notes and questions from input:

....

....

....

....

....

....

....

....

....

....

....

....

3. Three gifts and three strands

A. Three gifts

You've just heard a summary of what this course is about. Another way of summarizing the methodology of this course is that we will be trying to make the most of three incredible gifts that God has given us:

- God has given us **his word**, the Bible, to light our path like a torch on a dark night. It is good to share our thoughts, feelings and experiences—but in the end it's God who not only has the answers, but also knows which are the truly important questions.
- God also gives us **each other**—to help, to urge, to encourage and to

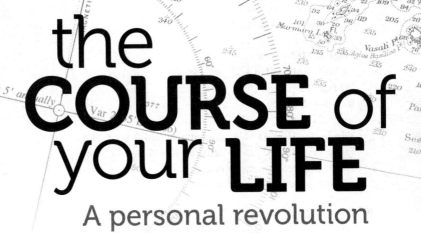

the
COURSE of
your **LIFE**

A personal revolution

Workbook

Tony Payne

The Course of Your Life: Workbook
© Matthias Media 2011

Matthias Media
(St Matthias Press Ltd ACN 067 558 365)
PO Box 225
Kingsford NSW 2032
Australia
Telephone: (02) 9663 1478; international: +61-2-9663-1478
Facsimile: (02) 9663 3265; international: +61-2-9663-3265
Email: info@matthiasmedia.com.au
Internet: www.matthiasmedia.com.au

Matthias Media (USA)
Telephone: 330 953 1702; international: +1-330-953-1702
Facsimile: 330 953 1712; international: +1-330-953-1712
Email: sales@matthiasmedia.com
Internet: www.matthiasmedia.com

ISBN 978 1 921896 34 7

Cover design and typesetting by Matthias Media.

Contents

sharpen each other. You'll spend lots of time in the Bible during this course, and you'll do most of it together rather than individually.

- We also need God to work in our hearts and minds to help us understand and change. That's why **prayer** is such a precious gift— God invites us to come to him and ask him to work in our lives, and he promises to give us only good gifts in response to our prayers.

The Course of Your Life is built on these three gifts from God, and consists of three interconnected components or strands.

B. Three strands

i. Seminars

- Around 90 minutes in length.
- Addressing key topic areas by doing Bible research together, pulling ideas together, and praying together.
- There are nine seminars (including this opening one).

ii. One-to-one meetings

- With one other person, to read and pray together.
- Focusing on Paul's letter to the Colossians.
- Complementing and supporting the topics covered in the seminars.
- Providing opportunity to talk privately about what you're learning and being challenged by.

iii. Intensive

- Towards the end of the course (usually between seminars 8 and 9).
- Can be two days away together, or over consecutive Saturdays, or similar.
- Integrating and completing the course content.
- Providing time and space to think through the implications for different aspects of your own lives, and to pray.

The course has been designed so that these three strands interconnect and reinforce each other. The passages you study in your one-to-one meetings will feed into the seminar discussions, and the intensive will draw upon all the material that has been done in the one-to-one meetings and the seminars.

All this will take time and require a little patience. We won't answer every question by the end of seminar 3. If at various points in the course you feel a little frustrated, or even confused, that's not altogether a bad thing! A serious rethinking of our lives is not the easiest thing in the world to do. In God's grace, by the end of the course we hope and trust that you will have reached a new clarity.

4. More about the one-to-one meetings

For some of you, this may be the first time you've ever read the Bible one-to-one. Don't worry—it's not very difficult! And to make it even easier, we've provided you with a simple framework to use each time. This basically consists of:

- having a quick catch-up about what is happening in your life
- praying and giving thanks together briefly
- reading and discussing the Bible together for about 30 minutes (using the provided template/material)
- praying to conclude.

By far the most difficult thing about meeting one-to-one to read the Bible is… actually meeting. This is like Bible reading in general. The hardest aspect of personal Bible reading is usually just being disciplined enough to sit down, open the Bible and start reading. It's the same with meeting one-to-one. Working out a convenient time and then sticking to it—that's the key.

Once you're there it's really not that hard, and almost always very rewarding.

To make the meetings as convenient as possible, your course leader has tried to pair you up with someone who either lives or works close to you.

5. Meet your one-to-one partner

A. Start by working out a suitable time and place for your first meeting—which needs to happen before seminar 2. (This might turn into your regular meeting time. You can sort that out when you get together.)

B. Share a little bit about yourself with your partner by answering one of the following questions:

- When you were 18 (which might have been 3 or 30 years ago!), did you have any dreams or goals in life? Have they been met?
- Can you think of a major mistake you have made in your life? What were the consequences?
- Think back to a reasonably major life decision you have made in the last five years (relating to work, family, friends, church, etc.). What were the key factors that determined your decision? What process did you go through in making up your mind?

C. Read Psalm 139:1-16 aloud together.

(i) What does this passage say about God's place in the course of our lives?

(ii) How does the psalmist feel about this? How does he react?

(iii) How do you react?

Seminar 2
God's creative purposes

1. Bible research: God and his world

A. In your subgroups, read Genesis 1-2. As you read, think about the following two questions:

(i) Why did God make the world? What clues do we get here about his purposes or intentions?

(ii) More specifically, why did he make humanity? What purposes did he have in mind?

Spend a few minutes discussing your answers to these two questions.

B. Divide the following passages among the groups and fill in the table described below (you'll need to draw a larger version on the sheets of paper provided by your course leader). Select from:

Isaiah 14:24-27	Psalm 33
Isaiah 45:5-10	Proverbs 16:4
Isaiah 46:8-11	Acts 17:24-27
Isaiah 55:6-11	Revelation 4:11
Psalm 8	

As you do this exercise:
- Look up each passage as a group, and read it aloud.
- Choose one person to be the scribe.
- When questions arise, jot them in the 'question' column, but don't pause to discuss them (at this point).
- You won't be able to put things in every column for each passage.
- Keep moving quickly, and allow 5-10 minutes at the end of the exercise to do part C.

Draw up a table as follows. In each column jot down quickly what you learn about that subject in the Bible passages you have selected.

Passage	What do we learn about God the creator?	What do we learn about God's purposes or intentions?	What do we learn about ourselves?	Other notes and questions

C. Still in your subgroups, try to summarize the most important points you've picked up from your Bible research under the following headings:

(i) What did you learn about God the creator?

(ii) What did you learn about God's purposes or intentions for his creation?

(iii) What did you learn about yourself?

(iv) What questions puzzled you most?

2. Group feedback

....
....
....
....
....
....
....
....
....

3. Input: Who are we?

Notes and questions from input:

....

....

....

....

....

....

....

....

....

....

4. Discussion and prayer

....

....

....

....

....

....

....

....

....

....

....

....

Seminar 3
What went wrong?

1. Input: What went wrong?

Notes and questions from input:

2. Bible research: The grim realities

A. Read Ecclesiastes 3.

   (i) What does this passage teach us about life?

   (ii) What do we know and understand?

   (iii) What do we **not** know and understand?

   (iv) Why has God put us in this situation?

   (v) What is the factor that renders all our striving a bit meaningless?

   (vi) So what does the Preacher recommend in the circumstances?

   (vii) If you were going to use Ecclesiastes 3 to give a nugget of wise advice about life to a child, what would it be?

B. Read Ecclesiastes 8:16-9:12.

   (i) What does this passage teach us about life?

(ii) What is the state of humanity's heart?

(iii) What can we **not** know or figure out?

(iv) What event frustrates our attempt to understand and to control our lives?

(v) What conclusions does the Preacher draw from this?

(vi) If you were going to use this passage to give a nugget of wise advice about life to a child, what would it be?

3. Group feedback

....

....

....

....

....

....

....

....

4. Input: Where to turn?

Notes and questions from input:

....

....

....

....

....

....

....

....

....

....

5. Discussion and prayer

....

....

....

....

....

....

....

....

....

....

....

....

....

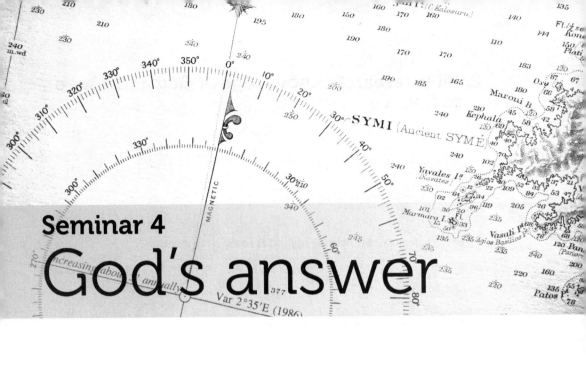

Seminar 4
God's answer

1. Input: God's answer

Notes and questions from input:

....
....
....
....
....
....
....
....
....
....
....
....
....
....
....
....

2. Bible research: Knowledge of God and where to find it

A. Read Psalm 19.

(i) How does God reveal himself?

(ii) What sort of knowledge of God is revealed in creation?

(iii) What should be our response to it?

(iv) What sort of knowledge is revealed in the law of the Lord?

(v) What should be our response to it?

B. Read Hebrews 1:1-4.

(i) How and when has God spoken in the past?

(ii) How has God spoken more recently?

(iii) What do you think "in these last days" means?

(iv) What else do we learn about the word that God has spoken in these last days?

C. Read 2 Peter 1:1-4.

(i) What has God given us?

(ii) Through what (or whom) has he given us this?

(iii) What is the end point or goal?

3. Input: God's sufficient word

Notes and questions from input:

a. God's sufficient word

b. God's agenda

....

....

....

....

....

....

....

....

....

....

....

....

4. Discussion and prayer: What does this mean for us?

....

....

....

....

....

....

....

....

....

....

....

....

....

Seminar 5
God's agenda

1. The story so far

2. Bible research: What is God's agenda?

Choose one of the following four passages and read it through a couple of times. Your goal in this exercise is to summarize in a paragraph or so what this passage tells you about God's agenda. What is God doing in the world? What is he focused on? What is his plan for the world and for us?

A. Acts 17:22-31

Questions that might help you:

- What is Paul's argument against idols and human religion?
- What does this passage say about how the world came to be the way it is? Was there a purpose to it being this way?
- If you were going to write a very short history of the world (in about four sentences) from this passage, what would it be?
- What part does Jesus play in this history?

Your summary of God's agenda:

B. Ephesians 1:1-10

Questions that might help you:

- Look for all the times Paul uses the phrase "in Christ" or "in him". What has God done in Christ?
- What's the timeline of this passage? When does it date from? And when does it go to?
- What is God's ultimate goal or purpose across all this span of time?
- When did this plan finally become known?

Your summary of God's agenda:

C. Colossians 1:1-20

Questions that might help you:

- In verses 3-6, the gospel almost has a life of its own. What is the gospel doing?
- What had the gospel done or produced in the Colossians' lives?
- What does Paul hope and pray they will continue in/grow in?
- Who is the Son? What is his place in God's plans?

Your summary of God's agenda:

D. Titus 2:11-14

Questions that might help you:

- What has happened in the past?
- What will happen in the future?
- What should happen in the meantime?
- What was the ultimate plan of "our great God and Saviour Jesus Christ"?

Your summary of God's agenda:

3. Group feedback

4. Input: The secret of life

Notes and questions from input:

....
....
....
....
....
....
....
....
....
....
....

5. Discussion and prayer

....
....
....
....
....
....
....

Seminar 6
Christ's death, my life

1. Input: Where are we up to?

We've seen that if God is the sovereign creator who has plans and intentions for this world, and if he has revealed these purposes in these last days by his Son, then what he has revealed in the Scriptures doesn't just add to my busy agenda—it rewrites it. The Bible reveals which matters matter. If we believe this, it will change the course of our lives.

If we were going to summarize God's agenda in our world from what we have seen so far, we could use the words of Colossians 1:13-14: God's cosmic purpose, his plan, his agenda in this world is **to glorify Jesus the Christ by transferring forgiven rebels like us out of the domain of darkness and into his eternal kingdom**. God's agenda is to unite all things in Jesus, to deliver people into the kingdom of Jesus, to glorify Jesus, to purify a people for Jesus, to appoint Jesus as the king of the universe, and for people everywhere to acknowledge Jesus as Lord.

But our pressing question is: how does God's agenda connect with the course of **our** lives?

And to understand that, we need to understand the key moment in God's unfolding plan: the death and resurrection of Jesus.

We need to take some time to understand it, because the death of Jesus is the point of intersection between God's agenda and our lives. It is through the death of Jesus that God's plan shapes the course of our lives.

2. Bible research: Explaining the cross

Imagine you invite a friend along to church one day, and they hear a talk that mentions Jesus' death. You're chatting afterwards, and when you ask them what they thought of the sermon, they say to you: "Well, to be honest, I don't really understand what all the fuss is about the crucifixion of Jesus. I can understand that he died, and that it was an act of sacrifice or something. But I can't really see what it's got to do with me and my life."

And then you say to them (in a moment of boldness and clarity), "Do you mind if I show you this passage I love in the Bible? It exactly answers your question about why Jesus' death is so important, and what it has to do with us and our lives."

Your Bible research exercise is to come up with an explanation from one of the following passages that would explain to your friend:

A. what Jesus' death really meant (i.e. what it achieved or why it was necessary)

B. what difference Jesus' death makes to us and to our lives (i.e. how it connects with us; how it affects us).

Romans 5:6-10
Colossians 2:11-15
1 Peter 2:22-25
2 Corinthians 5:17-21

A. What Jesus' death really meant:

B. What difference Jesus' death makes to us and to our lives:

3. Group feedback

Share your presentations with one another.

....

....

....

....

....

....

....

....

4. Input: Christ's death and ours

Notes and questions from input:

a. *Jesus our substitute*

....

....

....

....

....

....

b. *The love of Christ controls us*

....

....

....

....

....

....

c. Jesus our representative

....
....
....
....
....
....
....
....
....
....
....
....
....
....
....
....
....
....
....

5. Discussion and prayer

....
....
....
....
....
....
....
....

Seminar 7
Transformation

1. Discussion: Does it really matter how we live?

Imagine a Christian friend said something like this to you: "I kind of know that I should try to be godly in my life as a Christian, but to be honest I'm not that motivated. I know that Jesus has paid for my sins, and that God has forgiven me. And I know that when I sin in the future—which I will!—he will forgive me then as well. So does it really matter all that much if my godliness doesn't improve?"

Choose one person in the group to 'be' this person. Try to persuade him or her that it really does matter how we live our lives as Christians.

After you've done this for a few minutes, write down together the most effective or useful arguments and Bible passages that came up in your 'debate'.

2. Input: The logic of the Christian life

Notes and questions from input:

....

....

....

....

....

....

....

....

....

....

....

....

Because God's agenda is

  •

  •

then our agenda is

  •

3. Group discussion

....
....
....
....
....
....
....
....
....
....

4. Input: A killer's guide to sin

Notes and questions from input:

....
....
....
....
....

Three weapons:

1.

....
....
....
....
....

2.

3.

5. Discussion and prayer

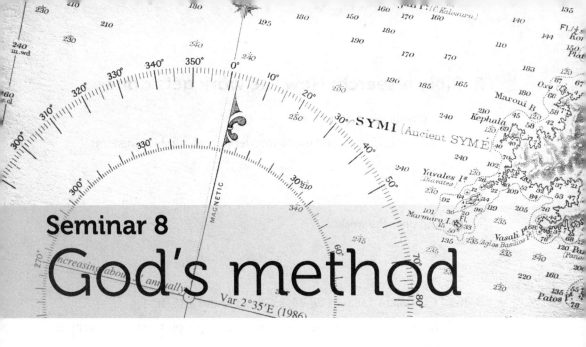

God's method

1. Introduction

We've seen that God's agenda in our world and for our lives is to transfer forgiven rebels like us out of darkness into his eternal kingdom, and to transform us towards maturity in Christ as we wait for his return, and thus bring great glory to his Son.

We've also seen that this worldwide plan and agenda of God intersects with our own lives as we put our faith in Christ; as we are united with him in his death and raised up to a new life in him.

And in our last seminar, we saw that we take part in God's agenda in our lives by setting our minds and hearts on Christ above, and therefore by putting sin to death and clothing ourselves with the character of Christ.

But there is another question that we haven't really faced yet: what is God's **method** for pursuing this great work of transferring and transforming? How is he doing it? What's his strategy, his approach?

We caught a glimpse of it towards the end of our last seminar when we talked about how we kill the sin in our lives.

But we need to explore this further.

2. Bible research: How the work gets done

A. Read Colossians 1:3-8 and 4:2-6.

(i) What method does God use to transfer people into his kingdom?

(ii) Who does the work?

B. Read Colossians 1:9-10, 1:28-29, 2:6-8, 3:1-4 and 3:15-16.

(i) What means does God use for transforming people towards maturity in Christ?

(ii) Who does the work?

C. See if you can summarize what God's method is for pursuing his agenda in people's lives.

D. Now look up the following passages. What do they say about the role of every Christian in advancing God's agenda in the world?

- Matthew 28:16-20

- Romans 15:14-15

- 1 Corinthians 10:31-11:1

- 1 Corinthians 14:26

- 1 Corinthians 15:58, 16:10

- Philippians 1:3-7

- Philippians 1:27-30

- Philippians 4:14-19

- Hebrews 3:12-13

E. What conclusions would you draw from these passages?

F. How do you think the role of every Christian relates to the role of people with particular gifts or responsibilities (like pastors, teachers, and so on)?

G. How do you feel about your conclusions? Do any problems or obstacles spring to mind?

3. Input: God's strategy involves us

Notes and questions from input:

....

....

....

....

Three P's:

P ....

....

P ....

....

P ....

....

Because God's agenda is
- *to transfer*

- *and to transform*

then our agenda is
- *to*

- *and to*

4. Discussion and prayer

....

....

....

....

....

Intensive

Part 1: Where we're up to

1. The story so far

See if you can complete the following summary of the course so far—from memory. If not, have a quick look back at each seminar in your workbook.

Seminar 2: God's creative purposes

A. What were God's purposes for humanity in creation?

B. We are God's creatures, created by him for particular reasons. What then should be our basic attitude or response towards God?

C. What does all this mean for the plans and agenda we have for our lives?

Seminar 3: What went wrong?

A. What was the essence of humanity's rebellion against God?

B. What was God's judgement against us?

C. Ecclesiastes spells out the realities of a world under God's judgement. What are the particular implications for the plans and dreams we have for our life here on earth?

Seminar 4: God's answer

A. God has an answer to the absurdity, injustice and evil of our judged world. In what three ways is this answer revealed?

B. What does 'the sufficiency of Scripture' mean?

C. What are the implications of the sufficiency of Scripture for understanding the agenda of our lives?

Seminar 5: God's agenda

A. What is God's ultimate plan or agenda for the world? How would you summarize it?

B. How does God's agenda address the basic problem of our world and our lives?

Seminar 6: Christ's death, my life

A. What does Paul mean in 2 Corinthians 5:14-15 when he says, "one has died for all, therefore all have died"?

B. How does this motivate us in our daily lives?

Seminar 7: Transformation

A. If our old self has died in Christ, why does sin still persist in our lives?

B. What is the basic motivation for seeking to kill sin in our lives, and to clothe ourselves in Christlike character?

C. How would you summarize God's agenda for our lives?

Seminar 8: God's method

A. What are the three P's by which God pursues his agenda in the world?

B. What is the role of every Christian in God's work in the world?

C. See if you can complete the summary of God's agenda that we came up with in seminar 8:

Because God's agenda is

- to _____ us into _____
- and to _____ us to be _____

then our agenda is

- to _____ towards _____ by prayerfully

  _____

- and to move _____ towards _____ by prayerfully

  _____.

Unanswered questions

Do you have any major unanswered questions arising out of the course so far?

- Things we've covered that you don't understand or aren't sure about

- Things we haven't covered yet

2. Group feedback

Part 2: The disciple's commission

1. Bible study: Matthew 28:16-20

Read Matthew 28:16-20.

A. What has the resurrected Jesus been given?

B. What does he tell his disciples to do, and in what time frame?

C. What do you think is the connection between your answers to A and B?

D. Is there anything in the passage to suggest that Jesus' command:
- only applies to the eleven disciples who first heard it?

- might apply to all his disciples?

2. Input: The disciple's commission

Notes and questions from input:

a. Matthew 28 and the disciple's commission

....

....

....

....

....

....

b. Making disciples one step at a time

....

....

....

Domain of darkness | **Kingdom of the Son**

Transfer and transform

Maturity in Christ

3. Step by step

There are so many ways that we can move people step by step towards maturity in Christ, no matter where they are on the spectrum. Here are some examples:

- Sarah's teenage son is having real problems at school, and as they talk about it at night, she reassures him that God is stronger and more faithful than any friend, and prays with him.

- Bill is chatting to George after church, and shares with him how encouraged he was by a particular verse in the Bible that day.
- Michael meets every fortnight over breakfast with his mate Steve, who is a newish Christian. They use the *Just for Starters* studies to work through some of the basic issues of the Christian life.
- Warren goes to a Bible study group each week at Jim's house with six other people. He makes sure that he has read and thought about the passage before he goes, and prays that God would help him to say true and encouraging things in the group.
- Irene is quite elderly and finds it hard to get out, but she phones her friend Jean every second day, talks to her about the Bible passage she has read that morning, and prays with her over the phone.
- Clare has been praying for her friend Shirley for months, and finally invites her to an evangelistic evening that her church is running. On the way home in the car, Clare talks to Shirley about the message, and does her best to answer Shirley's questions.
- Trevor rearranges his work schedule so that he can take each Wednesday morning off to teach Scripture classes in his local primary school. He and his wife end up doing this for many years, having an enormous impact on the lives of kids and teachers at their local school.
- At Phil's church, they take a few minutes each week during the Sunday meeting for a congregation member to give a testimony or to bring an encouraging word to the congregation. This Sunday it's Phil's turn, and he explains how the teaching of Ephesians 5 has turned his marriage around.[1]

Try coming up with some ideas of your own. Think of someone you know (Christian or non-Christian). What could you do to move them a step or two closer to Christ, and to maturity in Christ?

....

....

....

....

....

1   Taken from Colin Marshall and Tony Payne, *The Trellis and the Vine*, Matthias Media, Sydney, 2009, pp. 54-55.

Part 3: God's agenda and our work

1. Input: What about work?

Notes and questions from input:

....

....

....

....

....

....

....

....

2. Bible survey: The good and bad of work

A. Divide up the following Bible passages among your groups, and fill in the table. Not every passage will have something to say under each heading.

Passage	Good things about work	Not-so-good things about work	Good attitudes or approaches to work	Poor attitudes or approaches to work
Gen 11:1-9				
Eccl 2:1-11				

Eccl 2:18-26				
Eccl 4:4-8				
Eccl 5:18-20				
Eccl 9:9-10				
Prov 12:14				
Prov 18:9				
Prov 21:25				
Prov 23:4				

Prov 24:27				
Luke 12:13-31				
Eph 4:28				
2 Thess 3:6-12				
Col 3:22-24				
Jas 4:13-16				

B. Come back together as one whole group and pool your findings.

(i) What's good about work?

(ii) What's hard or difficult about work?

(iii) What wise or good attitudes or approaches to work did you find?

(iv) What harmful, wrong or foolish attitudes or approaches to work did you discover?

C. How does the Bible's teaching fit with your own experience of work?
(i) What do you enjoy about work?

(ii) What do you find difficult?

(iii) What good approaches to work have you observed or practised?

(iv) What poor or wrong attitudes have you observed or fallen into?

3. Input: Our work and God's agenda

Notes and questions from input:

....

....

....

....

....

....

....

Part 4: Talk and pray

1. Let's talk

In our last session, we covered lots of ground and raised plenty of meaty issues. Now we're going to take some time to talk through our questions, and to pray.

A. We talked about two common mistakes Christians make in thinking about their work. The first is the mistake of Babel and of the rich fool: to invest our work, and the fruits of our work, with too much significance; to make 'a successful career' the main agenda item of our life.

(i) How does this attitude tend to show itself, do you think—in our day-to-day lives as well as in the bigger decisions we make?

(ii) Where do you see this tendency in yourself (if at all)?

(iii) What can you do about it?

B. The other common problem is to seal our work life off from God, as if it doesn't matter to him what we do between 9 and 5 each day.

(i) How would this attitude show itself?

(ii) Where do you see this tendency in yourself (if at all)?

(iii) What can you do about it?

C. A Christian friend says to you: "I want to glorify God in my work, which means I'm going to strive for excellence and success in my field. I want to honour him by being the best I can be." How would you respond?

D. Spend some time talking about how you think God wants us to pursue his agenda in our lives as we go to work each day, based on what we have looked at in the course so far.

(i) In what ways could you press forward towards maturity in Christ in the way you work? What sins do you need to put to death? What Christlike character do you need to put on?

(ii) How could you move others towards maturity in Christ at your work? Who do you relate to often at work? How could you move them one step forwards?

E. Pray together about the challenges of your work lives. Share the particular struggles you have, and ask God to help you live out his agenda at work.

2. Taking it further

Boiling it all down, we could summarize our discussion of work like this:

A. **Work** is a good creation of God for our benefit and growth. And even though **work** is marred by sin and the Fall, we still find joy and satisfaction in it, and should receive it as God's good gift with thanksgiving.

B. It is possible to misuse this gift by using our devotion to **work** to assert our independence from God; by making success and satisfaction in our **work** the real goal and agenda of our lives; by partitioning our **work** off from God and his agenda for our lives.

C. But God's agenda is for every aspect of our lives. It overlays and permeates everything we do. So God wants us to view our **work** as one of the areas in life in which we pursue his agenda, not ours—by pursuing Christlikeness in all that we do at **work**, and by seeking to move others in our **workplace** towards Christ as we relate to them.

D. This agenda influences not only how we behave in our **workplace**, but also the decisions we make about **work**—how much time we devote to it, how ambitiously we pursue it, and what we're prepared to give up in order to gain success.

This basic pattern of biblical thinking can be applied to nearly every other important area of our lives. For example, read back through the four points above, and replace the words '**work**' and '**workplace**' with the word '**family**'.

You can try the same exercise with '**sport**' or '**music**' or '**education**' (making adjustments here and there). All of these good gifts of God can also end up being a means of actually rebelling against God and writing our own agenda in life.

Choose one of these areas that is particularly relevant to you as a group, and work through the following questions.

A. It's possible to invest _____ with too much significance; to make success and happiness in _____ the main agenda item of our life.

(i) How does this attitude tend to show itself, do you think—in our day-to-day lives as well as in the bigger decisions we make?

(ii) Where do you see this tendency in yourself (if at all)?

(iii) What can you do about it?

B. The other common problem is to seal our _____ life off from God, as if it doesn't matter to him how we behave or how we relate to people when we are _____.

(i) How would this attitude show itself?

(ii) Where do you see this tendency in yourself (if at all)?

(iii) What can you do about it?

C. Spend some time talking about how you think God wants us to pursue his agenda in our lives through _____, based on what we have looked at in the course so far.

(i) In what ways could you press forward towards maturity in Christ in this area? What sins do you need to put to death? What Christlike character do you need to put on?

(ii) How could you move others towards maturity in Christ in your _____? Who could you move one step forwards? What's the next thing you could do for or with them?

D. Pray together about the challenges of your _____ lives. Share the particular struggles you have, and ask God to help you live out his agenda in this area.

Part 5: We're in this together

1. Introduction

So far in *The Course of Your Life*, we've talked a lot about God and his plan or agenda for our lives. But we've done this mostly at an individual level, thinking about the course of our own particular lives.

But of course, we're not isolated individuals. We are each part of a network of families and neighbourhoods and friends. And as Christians, we are part of God's people. We have brothers and sisters in Christ. We have church.

How does church fit into the agenda that God has for each one of us? That's what we'll look at in this session. Let's start by looking at some key Bible passages about church.

2. Bible survey: What's church about?

In the New Testament, the Greek word that we translate as 'church' in our English Bibles is *ekklesia*. In the language of the time, it was an everyday word that meant 'gathering' or 'assembly'. So in Acts 19 where there is a riot in the city of Ephesus, the word *ekklesia* is used to describe both the unruly crowd who is outraged by Paul's teaching, and the regular assembly that gets together to discuss civic matters:

> Now some cried out one thing, some another, for the **assembly** was in confusion, and most of them did not know why they had come together. (Acts 19:32)

> If therefore Demetrius and the craftsmen with him have a complaint against anyone, the courts are open, and there are proconsuls. Let them bring charges against one another. [39] But if you seek anything further, it shall be settled in the regular **assembly**. (Acts 19:38-39)

The word translated 'assembly' in these passages is the same one that is translated 'church' in most other passages in the New Testament. The word simply means a gathering, a get-together, an assembly, a congregation.

What we need to investigate then is this: what is the nature of the **Christian** assembly or congregation? What is distinctive about it? Why do Christians gather, and what should Christians do when they are assembled?

Look through the following passages, and write down anything you can discover about the nature of the Christian gathering (or 'church'), and what sorts of things we should do when we gather.

Passage	What is the nature of the Christian assembly?	What should Christians do when they gather?
Matt 16:16-18		
Rom 12:3-8		
1 Cor 1:2		
1 Cor 14:26-33		
Eph 4:11-16		
Col 3:12-17		
1 Tim 4:11-16		

Heb 10:24-25		
Heb 12:18-24		

A. How would you summarize the nature of the Christian gathering?

B. What are the key things we should do when we gather?

3. Input: Understanding church

Notes and questions from input:

....
....
....
....
....
....
....
....
....

4. Implications

A. If this is the biblical vision of church, practically speaking what should we do when we gather as a church?

B. Does what we have seen in this session challenge your own attitudes about church? If so, how?

C. When you're in your church gatherings, what could you do to encourage others and help them to move forward in Christ?

(i) Before you get there

(ii) During the main part of the meeting

(iii) As you chat afterwards

D. Pray for your church.

Part 6: Reflect, share, pray

1. Reflect

Here's the *Course of Your Life* summary that we've been working on:

> **Because God's agenda is**
> - **to transfer us into Christ's kingdom**
> - **and to transform us to be like Christ**
>
> **then our agenda is**
> - **to press forward towards maturity in Christ by prayerfully setting our minds on God's word**
> - **and to move others towards maturity in Christ by prayerfully speaking God's word to them.**

Spend some time on your own thinking about the following questions, and then praying about what you've written.

A. Where are you up to in growing towards maturity in Christ? Are there areas in which you have been particularly challenged this weekend?

B. What are the next steps for you personally in pressing towards maturity in Christ? Which of these steps will be hardest?

C. Think about the people in your life: at home, at work, in your family, in your friendship networks, and at church. Who do you want to move towards Christ and towards maturity in him? Be a bit specific. Write down one or two names in each area, and think of some things you could do for each person.

	Name	How could I move them forwards?
Home		
Work		
Family		
Friends		
Church		

D. Think about the overall shape of your life. How might advancing God's agenda reorder the priorities and structures in your life?

E. What's the simple, no-brainer thing that you could implement as a result of what you have learned in this intensive?

F. Be ready to share: in the next section, you'll each have an opportunity to encourage others in the group by sharing some of the things you've written down above. You might like to tell the group:

- the thing that challenged you most in this intensive

- the changes you'll find hardest to make

- the steps you'd like to take in helping others move towards maturity in Christ

- or something else entirely!

2. Share and pray

Where to now?

1. Discussion: Heads, hearts and hands

As we look back over all that we've learned and all that we've done, one way to draw it together is to say that we have been addressing our heads, hearts and hands.

Let's start by talking about our heads and our hearts.

A. Heads

We've covered a lot of Bible material during our time together. We could summarize much of it with the statement that we've been looking at in seminar 8 and during the intensive:

Because God's agenda is
- **to transfer us into Christ's kingdom**
- **and to transform us to be like Christ**

then our agenda is
- **to press forward towards maturity in Christ by prayerfully setting our minds on God's word**
- **and to move others towards maturity in Christ by prayerfully speaking God's word to them.**

Looking back over the **content** of the course, what have you learned that is new or striking? How has your understanding or knowledge grown—about

God and his plans, and about yourself and your life?

B. Hearts

This understanding of what God wants us to do with the rest of our lives is very challenging. It confronts and opposes the worldly goals and priorities that most of us have in our hearts.

- How has the course challenged your priorities and goals in life? In what ways has your heart been changed?

- What are the areas of sin in your life that you've been challenged about during the course? What do you need to "put to death"? What aspects of Christlikeness do you especially need to adopt?

C. Prayer

We'll come back to our 'hands' below. But first, spend some time praying in your groups about the matters you've shared.

2. Input: Where to from here?

Notes and questions from input:

....

....

....

....

....

....

3. Getting our hands dirty

Over the duration of the course, we've addressed our heads and our hearts, but also our hands. We've learned a practical skill—that is, how to read the Bible one-to-one with someone else.

- How did you feel about the one-to-one meetings before you started them? What have you learned along the way?

- What was your favourite method of reading one-to-one—question and answer, the Swedish method or COMA?

- Think about who you might invite to read the Bible with you—for example, a Christian friend at church, a non-Christian friend, your housemate, your spouse, your kids. Jot down some possibilities.

- Pray together that God would open the way for you to start a Bible reading partnership with someone in the next month.

A useful resource

To consolidate what you've learned about one-to-one Bible reading, get yourself a copy of *One-to-One Bible Reading: a simple guide for every Christian* by David Helm.[2] It not only summarizes very neatly what you've been learning, but also gives lots of really useful suggestions about what to read with different people, and how to approach the different kinds of writing in the Bible (e.g. letters, poetry, narrative, prophecy, etc.). It's an excellent little tool, especially for those who lack confidence in reading the Bible with others.

4. The freedom of the future

The glorious thing about the course of our lives is that God gives us an agenda, but not a detailed script. We don't know all the details of how we are going to live out God's agenda in every aspect of our lives.

What we do know is that we don't embark on this adventure alone. God is with us by his Spirit as we encourage one another, share ideas, work in harness together, and pray for each other.

Conclude your time together by doing four things:
- Brainstorm together about all the different ways you could cooperate and help each other to advance God's agenda in the world. How could you help each other in moving people towards maturity in Christ? See how many ideas you can come up with.
- Talk together about how to follow through on the gains made in this course. How are you going to keep encouraging each other? When are you going to meet again in order to talk and pray about how you're all going?
- Quickly look through appendix 1, or watch the video clip 'Matthias Media and God's agenda' (on the course DVD under 'Extra videos'). This provides a quick introduction to the many useful resources Matthias Media produces to help you pursue God's agenda.
- Pray as a group, giving thanks for all that you've learned, and asking God to bless your plans and efforts by his Spirit.

2 Matthias Media, Sydney, 2011

One-to-one meetings

Introduction

The Course of Your Life basically revolves around reading, studying, exploring and absorbing God's word—and being profoundly challenged and changed by what we find there.

However, in his wise and gracious way, God has given us not only his word (in the Bible), but also each other. We are able to learn from each other, to be challenged and pushed by each other, and to pray for each other.

The one-to-one component of *The Course of Your Life* brings these two gifts of God together in a simple, powerful way: two people reading the Bible together, helping each other to see what God is saying there, and praying for each other that you might obey what you hear.

Here are some simple guidelines to help you make the most of your one-to-one meetings:

1. **Find a mutually convenient time** that you can use as your regular meeting time for the duration of the course—over breakfast, at lunchtime, after work, on Sunday afternoons, or whenever. Your course leader has tried to pair you with someone who either lives or works relatively close to you, to make the process easier.

2. **There is no preparation** to be done before you get together. The personal readings that you do on your own will relate to the one-to-one meetings, but there is no formal 'homework' or set reading to do before you get together.

3. **There is no leader.** You are just two people getting together to help each other learn from the Bible.

4. Try to keep your one-to-one meetings to **under an hour**. Here's a suggested time frame for each of your meetings:
   - 5 mins: chat, get some coffee, talk about how you're going.
   - 10 mins: share one thing each that you'd like to give thanks for, and one thing each that you'd like to pray for. Then pray together. If you meet together in a place where praying feels awkward, try to find a better place! If that's not possible then just keep your prayers brief, and commit to pray for each other later on your own.
   - 30 mins: read the passage together (perhaps reading aloud half each) and then talk through what it means, and how it applies to your lives.
   - 5 mins: finish with prayer arising from the passage.

5. **Have conversations, not monologues.** The idea is to hear what God is saying in the Bible. Try to avoid giving your opinions at length, or getting on to your hobbyhorses.

6. **Don't be afraid to ask questions.** If you notice something that you don't understand or that doesn't seem to make sense, don't gloss over it. Focus in on it. See if you can answer it by looking more closely, especially at the rest of the passage. (It's very often by unlocking the things we don't really understand in a passage that the whole thing starts to make sense.)

7. For some of you, meeting one-to-one to read the Bible will be **a new experience**. To make it as simple as possible for you to get started, we've provided guidelines for each meeting (questions to answer, exercises related to the passage). Don't feel limited or constrained by the questions. They are there to stimulate your discussion together about the passage. As you go along, you may find that you don't really need to stick to the suggested questions or lines of enquiry, and that you'd prefer to delve into the passage in your own way. Go for it!

One other thing: you'll notice that we've printed out the passage for study. This not only makes it easy for you to take just this booklet with you to your one-to-one meetings, but it also ensures that you both have the same Bible translation in front of you. This makes reading the Bible together much easier!

One-to-one meeting 1

Colossians 1:1-14

1. Give yourselves a few minutes to settle in, get some food and drink (if appropriate), and chat. Share one thing each that you'd like to give thanks for to God, and one thing that you're anxious about and would like to bring before God in prayer. Then pray for each other.

2. Read Colossians 1:1-14 together.

Paul, an apostle of Christ Jesus by the will of God, and Timothy our brother,

² To the saints and faithful brothers in Christ at Colossae:

Grace to you and peace from God our Father.

³ We always thank God, the Father of our Lord Jesus Christ, when we pray for you, ⁴ since we heard of your faith in Christ Jesus and of the love that you have for all the saints, ⁵ because of the hope laid up for you in heaven. Of this you have heard before in the word of the truth, the gospel, ⁶ which has come to you, as indeed in the whole world it is bearing fruit and increasing—as it also does among you, since the day you heard it and understood the grace of God in truth, ⁷ just as you learned it from Epaphras our beloved fellow servant. He is a faithful minister of Christ on your behalf ⁸ and has made known to us your love in the Spirit.

⁹ And so, from the day we heard, we have not ceased to pray for you, asking that you may be filled with the knowledge of his will in all spiritual wisdom and understanding, ¹⁰ so as to walk in a manner worthy of the Lord, fully pleasing to him, bearing fruit in every good work and increasing in the knowledge of God. ¹¹ May you be strengthened with all power, according to his glorious might, for all endurance and patience with joy, ¹² giving thanks to the Father, who has qualified you to share in the inheritance of the saints in light. ¹³ He has delivered us from the domain of darkness and transferred us to the kingdom of his beloved Son, ¹⁴ in whom we have redemption, the forgiveness of sins.

3. Note down everything the passage says about:
- things that are past tense; things that happened in the past

- things that are in the present experience of the Colossians

- things that will happen in the future

4. Looking again over the passage, what do we learn about "the gospel"?
- Its content

- What it produces or achieves

5. Implications:
- When did the "word of the truth" first come into your life? What fruit do you think it has borne in and through you?

- What does this passage stimulate you to give thanks for, and to pray for?

6. Finish with thanksgiving and prayer.

One-to-one meeting 2

Colossians 1:15-20

1. After you've given yourselves a few minutes to settle in, get some food and chat, share one thing each that you'd like to thank God for, and one thing each that you're anxious about and would like to bring before God in prayer. Then pray for each other.

2. The questions below focus on verses 15-20, but to get the flow of things, read through Colossians 1:11-20.

> May you be strengthened with all power, according to his glorious might, for all endurance and patience with joy, [12] giving thanks to the Father, who has qualified you to share in the inheritance of the saints in light. [13] He has delivered us from the domain of darkness and transferred us to the kingdom of his beloved Son, [14] in whom we have redemption, the forgiveness of sins.
> [15] He is the image of the invisible God, the firstborn of all creation. [16] For by him all things were created, in heaven and on earth, visible and invisible, whether thrones or dominions or rulers or authorities— all things were created through him and for him. [17] And he is before all things, and in him all things hold together. [18] And he is the head of the body, the church. He is the beginning, the firstborn from the dead, that in everything he might be preeminent. [19] For in him all the fullness of God was pleased to dwell, [20] and through him to reconcile to himself all things, whether on earth or in heaven, making peace by the blood of his cross.

3. See if you can work out the logic of verses 15-20 by looking for the main connecting words (like 'for', 'and', but', 'that', etc.).

4. Write down everything that describes the relationship between the Son and:

- God

- all created things

- the church

(Tip: the term 'firstborn' in verses 15 and 18 basically means 'heir'. The firstborn son in the ancient world was the sole inheritor of his father's possessions. To be the 'firstborn' was to be one who inherited everything.)

5. Implications:

- According to this passage, what is the purpose of all created things? What does this mean for your own life?

- What does this passage stimulate you to give thanks for, and to pray for?

6. Finish with thanksgiving and prayer.

One-to-one meeting 3

Colossians 1:19-23

1. After you've given yourselves a few minutes to settle in, get some food and chat, share one thing each that you'd like to thank God for, and one thing each that you're anxious about and would like to bring before God in prayer. Then pray for each other.

2. Read through Colossians 1:19-29.

> For in him all the fullness of God was pleased to dwell, [20] and through him to reconcile to himself all things, whether on earth or in heaven, making peace by the blood of his cross.
>
> [21] And you, who once were alienated and hostile in mind, doing evil deeds, [22] he has now reconciled in his body of flesh by his death, in order to present you holy and blameless and above reproach before him, [23] if indeed you continue in the faith, stable and steadfast, not shifting from the hope of the gospel that you heard, which has been proclaimed in all creation under heaven, and of which I, Paul, became a minister.
>
> [24] Now I rejoice in my sufferings for your sake, and in my flesh I am filling up what is lacking in Christ's afflictions for the sake of his body, that is, the church, [25] of which I became a minister according to the stewardship from God that was given to me for you, to make the word of God fully known, [26] the mystery hidden for ages and genera-tions but now revealed to his saints. [27] To them God chose to make known how great among the Gentiles are the riches of the glory of this mystery, which is Christ in you, the hope of glory. [28] Him we proclaim, warning everyone and teaching everyone with all wisdom, that we may present everyone mature in Christ. [29] For this I toil, struggling with all his energy that he powerfully works within me.

3. What were the Colossians once like? What used to be their relationship to God?

4. Because of something that God has done, the situation or status of the Colossians has changed.

- What has changed? How is their situation different? (Compare Colossians 1:13—"He has delivered us from the domain of darkness and transferred us to the kingdom of his beloved Son".)

- How did this change come about? How was it achieved?

- What is the purpose or end result of this change?

5. What does this passage say about the role and response of the Colossians?

6. Implications:

- How do you see enmity or hostility to God expressed in the world around you?

- Thinking back over Colossians 1, where in the chapter do you see the theme of endurance or perseverance in Christ?

- What does this passage stimulate you to give thanks for, and to pray for?

7. Finish with thanksgiving and prayer.

One-to-one meeting 4

Colossians 1:24-2:5

1. Share with one another how you are going, and then pray briefly for each other and for your time together reading the Bible.

2. In this one-to-one meeting, you're going to try a slightly different way of reading the Bible together. It's called 'the Swedish method' (after the nationality of the person who made it popular), and it's very straightforward. You simply read the passage and then jot down some notes under three categories:

 A light bulb: anything that stands out in the passage as you read it—such as repeated words or phrases, or particularly striking ideas.

 A question mark: something that you don't understand or that puzzles you.

 An arrow: something that applies personally to your life.

Start by reading the passage: Colossians 1:24-2:5.

> Now I rejoice in my sufferings for your sake, and in my flesh I am filling up what is lacking in Christ's afflictions for the sake of his body, that is, the church, [25] of which I became a minister according to the stewardship from God that was given to me for you, to make the word of God fully known, [26] the mystery hidden for ages and generations but now revealed to his saints. [27] To them God chose to make known how great among the Gentiles are the riches of the glory of this mystery, which is Christ in you, the hope of glory. [28] Him we proclaim, warning everyone and teaching everyone with all wisdom, that we may present everyone mature in Christ. [29] For this I toil, struggling with all his energy that he powerfully works within me.
> [2:1] For I want you to know how great a struggle I have for you and for those at Laodicea and for all who have not seen me face to face,

[2] that their hearts may be encouraged, being knit together in love, to reach all the riches of full assurance of understanding and the knowledge of God's mystery, which is Christ, [3] in whom are hidden all the treasures of wisdom and knowledge. [4] I say this in order that no-one may delude you with plausible arguments. [5] For though I am absent in body, yet I am with you in spirit, rejoicing to see your good order and the firmness of your faith in Christ.

3. Now jot down one or two things next to each symbol below. Take a couple of minutes to do this on your own, and then:

- share your light bulbs with each other
- share your questions with each other (and see if you can come up with any answers)
- share your arrows with each other.

4. Finish with thanksgiving and prayer based on what you have learned and shared together from this passage.

One-to-one meeting 5

Colossians 2:6-15

1. Share with one another how you are going, and then pray briefly for each other and for your time together reading the Bible.

2. Read Colossians 2:6-15 and talk about it together using the Swedish method.

> Therefore, as you received Christ Jesus the Lord, so walk in him, [7] rooted and built up in him and established in the faith, just as you were taught, abounding in thanksgiving.
> [8] See to it that no-one takes you captive by philosophy and empty deceit, according to human tradition, according to the elemental spirits of the world, and not according to Christ. [9] For in him the whole fullness of deity dwells bodily, [10] and you have been filled in him, who is the head of all rule and authority. [11] In him also you were circumcised with a circumcision made without hands, by putting off the body of the flesh, by the circumcision of Christ, [12] having been buried with him in baptism, in which you were also raised with him through faith in the powerful working of God, who raised him from the dead. [13] And you, who were dead in your trespasses and the uncircumcision of your flesh, God made alive together with him, having forgiven us all our trespasses, [14] by cancelling the record of debt that stood against us with its legal demands. This he set aside, nailing it to the cross. [15] He disarmed the rulers and authorities and put them to open shame, by triumphing over them in him.

3. Jot down one or two things next to each symbol below. Take a couple of minutes to do this on your own, and then:
- share your light bulbs with each other
- share your questions with each other (and see if you can come up with any answers)
- share your arrows with each other.

4. Finish with thanksgiving and prayer based on what you have learned and shared together from this passage.

One-to-one meeting 6

Colossians 2:16-23

1. Share with one another how you are going, and then pray briefly for each other and for your time together reading the Bible.

2. Read Colossians 2:16-23 and talk about it together using the Swedish method.

> Therefore let no-one pass judgment on you in questions of food and drink, or with regard to a festival or a new moon or a Sabbath. [17] These are a shadow of the things to come, but the substance belongs to Christ. [18] Let no-one disqualify you, insisting on asceticism and worship of angels, going on in detail about visions, puffed up without reason by his sensuous mind, [19] and not holding fast to the Head, from whom the whole body, nourished and knit together through its joints and ligaments, grows with a growth that is from God.
>
> [20] If with Christ you died to the elemental spirits of the world, why, as if you were still alive in the world, do you submit to regulations— [21] "Do not handle, Do not taste, Do not touch" [22] (referring to things that all perish as they are used)—according to human precepts and teachings? [23] These have indeed an appearance of wisdom in promoting self-made religion and asceticism and severity to the body, but they are of no value in stopping the indulgence of the flesh.

3. Jot down one or two things next to each symbol below. Take a couple of minutes to do this on your own, and then:
- share your light bulbs with each other
- share your questions with each other (and see if you can come up with any answers)
- share your arrows with each other.

4. Finish with thanksgiving and prayer based on what you have learned and shared together from this passage.

One-to-one meeting 7

Colossians 3:1-4

1. Share with one another how you are going, and then pray briefly for each other and for your time together reading the Bible.

2. So far in your one-to-one meetings, you've used questions and answers (meetings 1-3), and the Swedish method (meetings 4-6). Now you're going try another way of reading the Bible together. It's called COMA, which stands for **c**ontext, **o**bservation, **m**eaning and **a**pplication. Start by reading Colossians 3:1-4.

> If then you have been raised with Christ, seek the things that are above, where Christ is, seated at the right hand of God. ² Set your minds on things that are above, not on things that are on earth. ³ For you have died, and your life is hidden with Christ in God. ⁴ When Christ who is your life appears, then you also will appear with him in glory.

3. Now read back over the passage and see what you can jot down together under the four COMA headings.

Context:
- Where is Paul up to in his argument? What has he just said in the previous few paragraphs?

Observation:

- Are there any major subsections or breaks in the text?
- What are the most important words or phrases? What is the main point or points?
- What surprises are there?

Meaning:

- How does this text relate to other parts of the book?
- How does the passage relate to Jesus?
- What does this teach you about God?
- How could you sum up the meaning of this passage in your own words?

Application:

- How does this passage challenge your understanding?
- Is there some attitude you need to change?
- How does this passage call on you to change the way you live?

4. Give thanks and pray based on what you have learned.

One-to-one meeting 8

Colossians 3:5-17

1. Share with one another how you are going, and then pray briefly for each other and for your time together reading the Bible.

2. Read Colossians 3:5-17.

> Put to death therefore what is earthly in you: sexual immorality, impurity, passion, evil desire, and covetousness, which is idolatry. [6] On account of these the wrath of God is coming. [7] In these you too once walked, when you were living in them. [8] But now you must put them all away: anger, wrath, malice, slander, and obscene talk from your mouth. [9] Do not lie to one another, seeing that you have put off the old self with its practices [10] and have put on the new self, which is being renewed in knowledge after the image of its creator. [11] Here there is not Greek and Jew, circumcised and uncircumcised, barbarian, Scythian, slave, free; but Christ is all, and in all.
>
> [12] Put on then, as God's chosen ones, holy and beloved, compassionate hearts, kindness, humility, meekness, and patience, [13] bearing with one another and, if one has a complaint against another, forgiving each other; as the Lord has forgiven you, so you also must forgive. [14] And above all these put on love, which binds everything together in perfect harmony. [15] And let the peace of Christ rule in your hearts, to which indeed you were called in one body. And be thankful. [16] Let the word of Christ dwell in you richly, teaching and admonishing one another in all wisdom, singing psalms and hymns and spiritual songs, with thankfulness in your hearts to God. [17] And whatever you do, in word or deed, do everything in the name of the Lord Jesus, giving thanks to God the Father through him.

3. Now read back over the passage and see what you can jot down together under the four COMA headings.

Context:

- Where is Paul up to in his argument? What has he just said in the previous few paragraphs?

Observation:

- Are there any major subsections or breaks in the text?
- What are the most important words or phrases? What is the main point or points?
- What surprises are there?

Meaning:

- How does this text relate to other parts of the book?
- How does the passage relate to Jesus?
- What does this teach you about God?
- How could you sum up the meaning of this passage in your own words?

Application:

- How does this passage challenge your understanding?
- Is there some attitude you need to change?
- How does this passage call on you to change the way you live?

4. Give thanks and pray based on what you have learned.

One-to-one meeting 9

Colossians 3:17-4:1

1. Share one thing each that you'd like to thank God for, and one thing each that you would like to bring before God in prayer. Then pray for each other.

2. Read Colossians 3:17-4:1 through twice.

> And whatever you do, in word or deed, do everything in the name of the Lord Jesus, giving thanks to God the Father through him. [18] Wives, submit to your husbands, as is fitting in the Lord. [19] Husbands, love your wives, and do not be harsh with them. [20] Children, obey your parents in everything, for this pleases the Lord. [21] Fathers, do not provoke your children, lest they become discouraged. [22] Bondservants, obey in everything those who are your earthly masters, not by way of eye-service, as people-pleasers, but with sincerity of heart, fearing the Lord. [23] Whatever you do, work heartily, as for the Lord and not for men, [24] knowing that from the Lord you will receive the inheritance as your reward. You are serving the Lord Christ. [25] For the wrongdoer will be paid back for the wrong he has done, and there is no partiality.
>
> [4:1] Masters, treat your bondservants justly and fairly, knowing that you also have a Master in heaven.

3. Without using any particular framework or method, talk together about what you think this passage is saying—its key points, its logic, its main idea—and then also talk about how it applies to your life. Jot down the key things you discover together, and then pray about them.

One-to-one meeting 10

Colossians 4:2-6

1. Share one thing each that you'd like to thank God for, and one thing each that you would like to bring before God in prayer. Then pray for each other.

2. Read Colossians 4:2-6 through twice.

> Continue steadfastly in prayer, being watchful in it with thanksgiving. [3] At the same time, pray also for us, that God may open to us a door for the word, to declare the mystery of Christ, on account of which I am in prison—[4] that I may make it clear, which is how I ought to speak.
> [5] Walk in wisdom toward outsiders, making the best use of the time. [6] Let your speech always be gracious, seasoned with salt, so that you may know how you ought to answer each person.

3. Without using any particular framework or method, talk together about what you think this passage is saying—its key points, its logic, its main idea— and then also talk about how it applies to your life. Jot down the key things you discover together, and then pray about them.

Appendix
Matthias Media and God's agenda

During this course we've developed a summary of God's agenda for the course of our lives. This is how we put it:

Because God's agenda is
- **to transfer us into Christ's kingdom**
- **and to transform us to be like Christ**

then our agenda is
- **to press forward towards maturity in Christ by prayerfully setting our minds on God's word**
- **and to move others towards maturity in Christ by prayerfully speaking God's word to them.**

Our mission at Matthias Media is basically to produce resources of all kinds that equip Christians to pursue God's agenda in their lives—to grow to maturity in Christ, and to minister to others to see them grow to maturity in Christ as well.

Below are listed some of our most popular and useful resources that can help you in pursuing God's agenda. For more details about these resources and many others, visit our website: **www.matthiasmedia.com**

Resources to help you press forward to maturity in Christ

The Briefing

Matthias Media has been publishing *The Briefing* in various formats for more than two decades. It's now available as a free online web magazine, as well as in a full-colour paper edition published six times a year and available by subscription. In *The Briefing* you'll find:

- Articles, audio and video to help Christians grow in their knowledge of God, and in their passion for godliness day by day.
- Ideas and examples to encourage all Christians in helping others grow towards maturity in Christ.
- A Christian perspective on the ideas and events of the world around us (including book reviews).
- Resources and ideas for pastors and other full-time gospel workers as they lead God's people in serving him.

For more information, visit the website: **matthiasmedia.com/briefing**

The Daily Reading Bible

The Daily Reading Bible is an all-in-one resource that helps you set your mind every day on God's word in the Bible.

Each volume contains around 60 undated readings. Each reading is designed to take around 15-20 minutes, and contains:

- the full text of the Bible passage for that reading
- some questions to get you thinking
- some 'points to ponder'
- some ideas to get you started in prayer.

It's all in one booklet that you can take with you anywhere—on the train, on the bus, to the park at lunchtime, or to your favourite armchair.

Guidebooks for Life

This is a series of straightforward, practical books that deal with the important nuts-and-bolts topics that Christians need to know about as we walk each day with our Master. Some Christian books are all theory and no practical application; others are all stories and tips with no substance. The Guidebooks for Life aim to achieve a vital balance—that is, to dig into the Bible and discover what God is telling us there, as well as apply that truth to our daily lives.

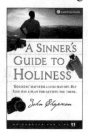

Key titles in the series include:
- *A Sinner's Guide to Holiness*, by John Chapman
- *Guidance and the Voice of God*, by Phillip Jensen and Tony Payne
- *Encouragement: How words change lives*, by Gordon Cheng

Resources to help you move others forward to maturity in Christ

Towards the end of *The Course of Your Life* we looked at the following diagram, which helps us to visualize our goal of helping others move forward, step by step, towards maturity in Christ:

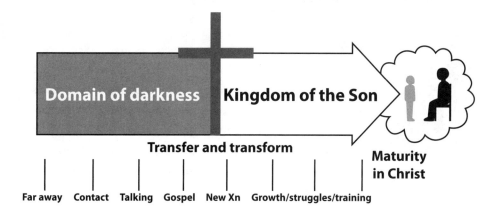

At Matthias Media, we divide all our resources into four categories that reflect this continuum of growth towards Christ:
- **Outreach**: talking about spiritual issues with our friends, and sharing the gospel with them
- **Follow-up**: establishing new and young Christians in the kingdom
- **Growth**: putting sin to death, and clothing ourselves with Christ's character
- **Training**: learning to serve others in **outreach**, **follow-up** and **growth**

Here are some of our key resources in each category.

Resources for outreach

The Essential Jesus

This innovative 80-page book combines a fresh translation of Luke's Gospel with an introduction and conclusion based on the well-known *Two Ways to Live* framework. The result is a very economical and effective way to share the gospel with lots of people.

Naked God

In *Naked God*, former lawyer Martin Ayers provides an opportunity for interested enquirers to examine the big questions: Is there a God? How can I know the truth given that different religions make different claims? And if there is a God, what real difference will he make to my life?

Two Ways to Live

Two Ways to Live is a memorable summary of the gospel that has been used to share the gospel with hundreds of thousands of people around the world. It comes in a range of styles, formats and languages, but each different resource that uses the *Two Ways to Live* framework features the same six-step logical presentation of what the Bible says about Jesus Christ. For more information, visit the website: **twowaystolive.com**

Resources for follow-up

Just for Starters

Used by thousands of churches worldwide, *Just for Starters* is widely regarded as **the** Bible study for following up new Christians. The seven studies look at what the Bible teaches on seven fundamental topics: Saved by God, Trusting in God, Living God's way, Listening to God, Talking to God, Meeting with God's family, Meeting the world.

There is a second set of studies in the series as well, called *Christian Living for Starters*.

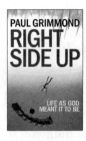

Right Side Up

This recent book by Paul Grimmond is especially designed for new Christians, to orient them to the new life they have embarked upon with Christ. It not only clearly explains the gospel (so that the foundations are solid), but also goes on to discuss the many practical issues and challenges that new believers face. It's a warm-hearted, engaging, exciting read about the adventure of the Christian life, and as such is a very helpful as a refresher for longer-serving Christians as well.

Resources for growth

Bible studies

We have two main series of Bible studies:
- Pathway Bible Guides: short, simple Bible studies that are easy to digest
- Interactive Bible Studies: solid food for more established Christians

Both series are designed mainly for small groups, although the Pathway series is also very suitable for one-to-one Bible study.

Although pitched at slightly different levels, both series focus closely on the passage of Scripture rather than bouncing too quickly into discussion or application; both seek to read the passage in its context; and both maintain a balance between providing input and direction, and allowing plenty of room for exploration and discovery.

Guidebooks for Life (with discussion guides)

Like many of our resources, the Guidebooks for Life series (described earlier) is not only excellent for seeking to grow ourselves; it is also an excellent tool for helping others grow. Get together with a friend (or in your small home group) and decide to read through one of these helpful books together, using the supplied discussion guide to stimulate your conversation together.

Resources for training

One-to-One Bible Reading: a simple guide for every Christian

You have already begun to learn about one-to-one Bible reading just by doing *The Course of Your Life*. This short, practical and very helpful book by David Helm will train you to take that ministry further. It provides lots of useful ideas about how to start reading the Bible with someone (whether Christian or non-Christian), along with a large range of resources and methods for reading different parts of the Bible. This is a supremely useful little book.

Two Ways to Live training

Our best-known training program is *Two Ways to Live: Know and share the gospel*. This seven-session course teaches participants to know the gospel thoroughly for themselves, and then trains them in how to explain that message clearly and naturally in their own words, using the well-known *Two Ways to Live* framework. With role-plays, DVD and audio input, the course is easy to run and highly effective.

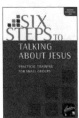

Six Steps courses

The other main plank in our training resources is the DVD-based Six Steps range, now with three titles in the series. Each one contains simple, straightforward training for every Christian in a basic area of Christian living and ministry:

- *Six Steps to Encouragement*: how to encourage one another with God's word
- *Six Steps to Talking About Jesus*: how to begin to share your faith with others
- *Six Steps to Reading your Bible*: how to dig into God's word for yourself

These courses are ideal for running in existing small groups as a framework for training people in knowledge, godliness and the ability to speak God's word to others for their growth in Christ.

Matthias Media is an evangelical publishing ministry that seeks to persuade all Christians of the truth of God's purposes in Jesus Christ as revealed in the Bible, and equip them with high-quality resources, so that by the work of the Holy Spirit they will:

- abandon their lives to the honour and service of Christ in daily holiness and decision-making
- pray constantly in Christ's name for the fruitfulness and growth of his gospel
- speak the Bible's life-changing word whenever and however they can—in the home, in the world and in the fellowship of his people.

It was in 1988 that we first started pursuing this mission, and in God's kindness we now have more than 300 different ministry resources being used all over the world. These resources range from Bible studies and books through to training courses and audio sermons.

To find out more about our large range of very useful resources, and to access samples and free downloads, visit our website:

www.matthiasmedia.com

How to buy our resources

1. Direct from us over the internet:
   – in the US: www.matthiasmedia.com
   – in Australia and the rest of the world: www.matthiasmedia.com.au

2. Direct from us by phone:
   – in the US: 1 866 407 4530
   – in Australia: 1800 814 360 (Sydney: 9663 1478)
   – international: +61-2-9663-1478

3. Through a range of outlets in various parts of the world. Visit www.matthiasmedia.com/contact for details about recommended retailers in your part of the world, including www.thegoodbook.co.uk in the United Kingdom.

4. Trade enquiries can be addressed to:
   – in the US and Canada: sales@matthiasmedia.com
   – in Australia and the rest of the world: sales@matthiasmedia.com.au

*Register at our website for our **free** regular email update to receive information about the latest new resources, **exclusive special offers**, and free articles to help you grow in your Christian life and ministry.*

Looking for something more?

If you're looking for more input for your Christian life and service, take a look at *The Briefing*.

more diversity

With a variety of columns and sections, and local and overseas perspectives, *The Briefing* offers plenty to readers in various stages and walks of life.

more content

Since *The Briefing* is available not just in print but also online, we can provide lots of content, including audio/video and new hosted blogs by gifted Christian thinkers and writers. Choose the content that is most relevant and useful to you.

more convenient

You can receive *The Briefing* in the way that best suits your reading habits—on the web, as an RSS feed, by pdf, as an email update, on your phone or smart device, and of course in print.

more social

Being online, *The Briefing* is share-able and discuss-able. So it's simple to connect your friends into *The Briefing* content via your favourite social networks.

more free

The remarkable thing about *The Briefing* is that it is all available free. Of course, if you want to have the beautiful paper edition mailed out to you then there is a small charge.

more information?

All the information you're likely to need, including subscription options, can be found at:

www.matthiasmedia.com/briefing